Peppa Pig™

Peppa Goes Boating

Peppa and her family have come to the lake to go boating.

"Boats! Boats! Get your boats here!"
calls Miss Rabbit.

"I've got canoes,"
says Miss Rabbit.
"Hmm . . ." says Daddy Pig.
"Paddling a canoe
is hard work."

"I've got sailing boats," says Miss Rabbit. Daddy Pig isn't sure. Sailing a sailing boat is a bit tricky.

"The pedalos look nice and relaxing," smiles Mummy Pig. "Yes!" agrees Daddy Pig. "They've got a big paddle wheel to make them go."

Daddy Pig, Mummy Pig, Peppa and George all climb onto a pedalo. "You have to pedal," Miss Rabbit tells them. "Enjoy your boat trip!" "Off we go!" shouts Daddy Pig. Peppa and George giggle. It's like a bicycle on the water!

Splish! Splosh!

Emily Elephant
and her family arrive.
"Hello Miss Rabbit,"
says Mr Elephant. "We'd
like a canoe please!"

"Certainly!" says Miss Rabbit.

"Ahoy there, Miss Rabbit!"
It's Danny Dog and his dad, Captain Dog!
They want to go out in a sailing boat.

"Aye, aye, Captain. I mean, Dad!" says Danny Dog.

"We're sailing!" shouts Danny.
"We're canoeing!" shouts Emily.
"We're pedalling!" shouts Peppa.

Hee!
Hee!

1

Poor Daddy Pig. Pedalling a pedalo is a lot harder than it looks.

It is time to stop for lunch.
Mummy Pig passes around the sandwiches.
"Here's some bread for you,
Mrs Duck," grins Peppa.
Mrs Duck likes picnics!

Quack!

Quack!

Everyone likes picnics!

Miss Rabbit
rings her bell.

Ding!
Dong!

"Come in boats one, two and three," she calls. "Your time is up!"

"One, two and three?" says Peppa. "That's us!"

"Let's see who can get back first," says Mummy Pig. "We'll have a race."

Everyone goes as fast as they can.
"I'm not sure I can pedal much
faster!" puffs Daddy Pig.
Captain Dog is lucky.
His boat has an engine.

Hooray!

"We win!" cries Danny. Captain Dog cheers.
"I'm not a sailor anymore," he says, "but I do love
boating on the lake!"